Saxmania!
Blues Greats.

Wise Publications
London/New York/Paris/Sydney

Exclusive Distributors:
Music Sales Limited
8/9 Frith Street,
London W1V 5TZ, England.
Music Sales Pty Limited
120 Rothschild Avenue,
Rosebery, NSW 2018,
Australia.

Book design by Pearce Marchbank Studio
Cover Photography by Julian Hawkins
Compiled by Peter Evans
Music arranged by Steve Tayton
Music processed by Upton And Skinner

Music Sales' complete catalogue lists thousands of titles and is free
from your local music shop, or direct from Music Sales Limited.
Please send a cheque/postal order for £1.50 for postage to:
Music Sales Limited, Newmarket Road, Bury St. Edmunds,
Suffolk IP33 3YB.

Printed in the United Kingdom by
Halstan & Co Limited, Amersham, Buckinghamshire.

And just look at some of the other music
you can play with Saxmania....

Saxmania! Standards
Includes 'Catch a Falling Star'...'As Time Goes By'...
'Pennies From Heaven'...
and thirty-one more golden favourites.
Order No. AM78262

Saxmania: Jazz Hits
Includes 'Mood Indigo'...'Take The 'A' Train'...'Take Five'...
and two dozen more all-time greats.
Order No. AM78254

Saxmania! Pop Greats
Includes 'Sailing'...'Stand By Me'...
'Nothing's Gonna Change My Love For You'...
and 29 more chart hits.
Order No. AM78247

Saxmania! Jazz Classics
Includes 'On The Sunny Side Of The Street'...
'Walking Shoes'...'Cute'...
and thirty other jazz classics.
Order No. AM90100

Saxmania! Rock Hits
Includes 'Addicted To Love'...'Layla'...'Roxanne'...
and twenty other rock classics.
Order No. AM90101

Fever

Words & Music by John Davenport & Eddie Cooley

Moderate jump beat (Snap fingers)

Tough Talk

By Joe Sample, Wayne Henderson & Bob "Stix" Hooper

Rock blues

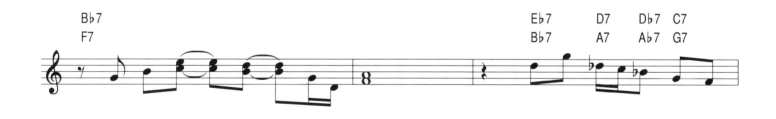

Hit The Road Jack

Words & Music by Percy Mayfield

Goodbye Pork Pie Hat

By Charles Mingus

Moderately slow

Mercy Mercy Mercy

Words by Gail Fisher Levy & Vincent Levy
Music by Josef Zawinul

Moderately slow with expression

Basin Street Blues

Words & Music by Spencer Williams

The Old Piano Roll Blues

Words & Music by Cy Coben

Ragtime tempo

Hey Lawdy Mama

Words & Music by Clive Reed

Slow blues tempo

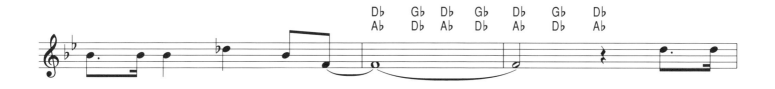

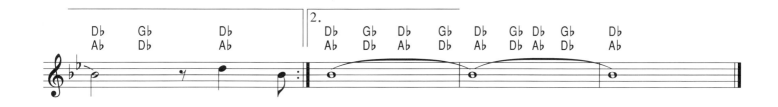

Learnin' The Blues

Words & Music by Dolores Vicki Silvers

With a solid beat

Blues In The Night (My Mama Done Tol'Me)

Words by Johnny Mercer
Music by Harold Arlen

Blues tempo

Cry Me A River

Words & Music by Arthur Hamilton

Slowly and Rhythmically

Eb Sax. | Fm | Db | Fm6 | Fm7 | Bbm7 | Cm | Eb7+
Bb Sax. | Cm | Ab | Cm6 | Cm7 | Fm7 | Gm | Bb7+

mf

Abmaj7 | Gm7 | C7 | Cm7 | Cdim | F7+ | Bb9
Ebmaj7 | Dm7 | G7 | Gm7 | Gdim | C7+ | F9

Bbm7 | Eb7 | Bbm7 | Ab6 | Abdim | Dbm | Cm | Cm6
Fm7 | Bb7 | Fm7 | Eb6 | Ebdim | Abm | Gm | Gm6

Fm6 | G7sus | G7 | Cm | Cm6 | Fm6 | G7
Cm6 | D7sus | D7 | Gm | Gm6 | Cm6 | D7

Cm | Cm6 | Fm6 | G7sus | G7 | C | C6
Gm | Gm6 | Cm6 | D7sus | D7 | G | G6

Gm7 | C7 | Fm | Db | Fm6 | Fm7
Dm7 | G7 | Cm | Ab | Cm6 | Cm7

Bbm7 | Cm | Eb7+ | Abmaj7 | Gm7 | C7 | Cm7 | Cdim | F7+
Fm7 | Gm | Bb7+ | Ebmaj7 | Dm7 | G7 | Gm7 | Gdim | C7+

Bb9 | Bbm7 | Eb7 | Bbm7 | Ab6
F9 | Fm7 | Bb7 | Fm7 | Eb6

Memphis Blues

Words & Music by W.C. Handy

Slow blues tempo

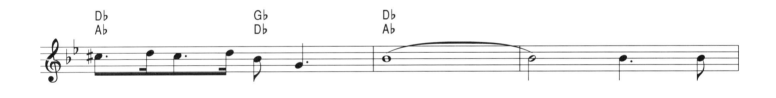

Sunny

Words & Music by Bobby Hebb

Moderate rock

Repeat and Fade

The Wang Wang Blues

Words by Leo Wood
Music by Gus Mueller, Buster Johnson & Henry Busse

Summertime Blues

Words & Music by Eddie Cochran & Jerry Capehart

Swingin' Shepherd Blues

Words by Rhoda Roberts & Kenny Jacobson
Music by Moe Koffman

Moderately slow

See See Rider

Words & Music By Gertrude "Ma" Rainey

Slow blues tempo

The Lady Sings The Blues

Words by Billie Holiday
Music by Herbie Nichols

Slow blues

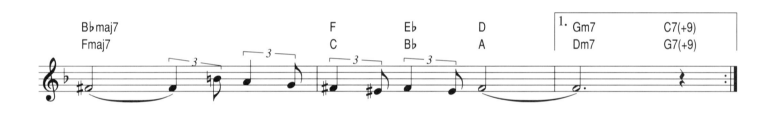

CODA

D. C. al Coda

25

The Lonesome Road

Words by Gene Austin
Music by Nathaniel Shilkret

Moderately

Just The Two Of Us

Words & Music by Ralph MacDonald, William Salter & Bill Withers

Mississippi Mud

Words & Music by Harry Barris

D. S. al Fine

Georgia On My Mind

Words by Stuart Gorrell
Music by Hoagy Carmichael

Blue And Sentimental

Words & Music by Count Basie, Jerry Livingston & Mack David

Tenor Madness

By Sonny Rollins

Alright, Okay, You Win

Words & Music by Sid Wyche & Mayme Watts

Walk On The Wild Side

Words by Mack David
Music by Elmer Bernstein

Blues (moderately slow 4)

Afro Blue

By Ramon "Mongo" Santamaria

Medium fast

Good Time Flat Blues

Words & Music by Spencer Williams

Moderato

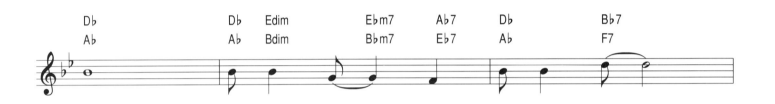

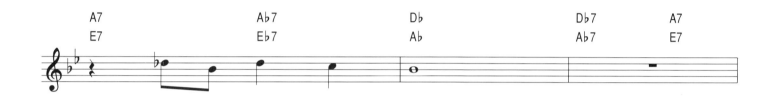

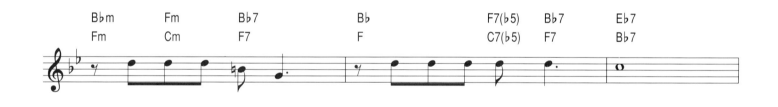

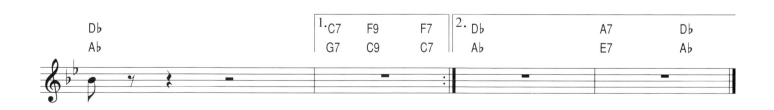

Limehouse Blues

Words by Douglas Furber
Music by Phil Braham

Medium bright

Lazy Bones

Words & Music by Johnny Mercer & Hoagy Carmichael

Slow blues

Is You Is, Or Is You Ain't (Ma' Baby)

Words & Music by Billy Austin & Louis Jordan

Moderately

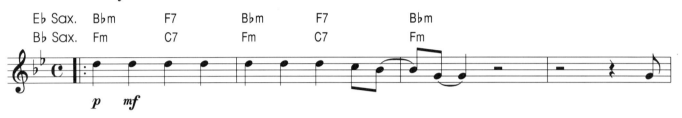

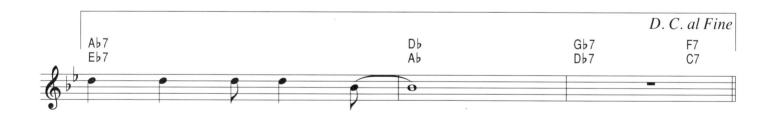

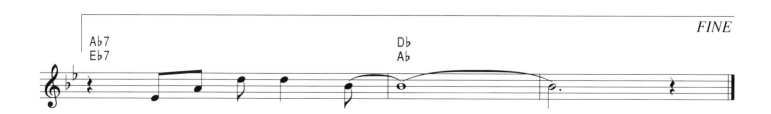

It Ain't Necessarily So

Music by George Gershwin

Moderately

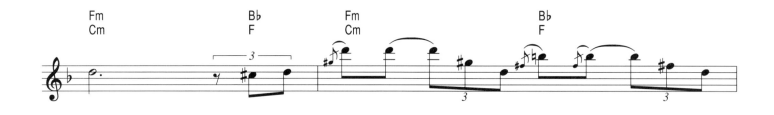

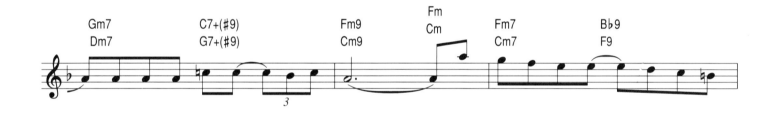

CODA

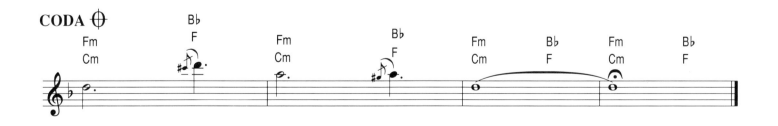

Straight No Chaser

By Thelonious Monk

Convolution

By Steve Tayton

Moderate swing blues

When Sunny Gets Blue

Words by Jack Segal
Music by Marvin Fisher

Slowly but rhythmically